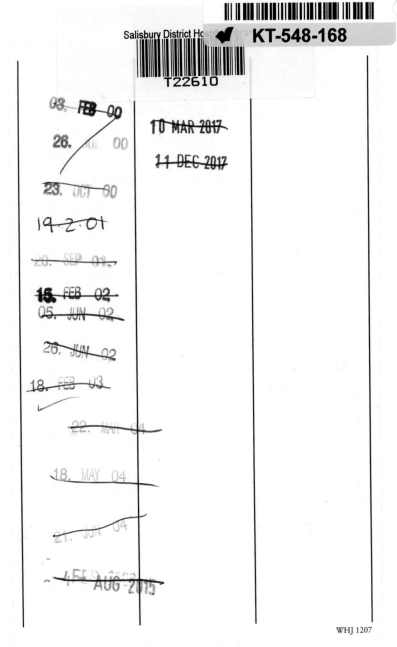

Stress Survival Guide

Stress Survival Guide

Caron Grainger

Honorary Clinical Lecturer
Institute of Public and Environmental Health
University of Birmingham

Senior Registrar in Public Health Medicine
Solihull Health Authority

BMJ
Publishing
Group

© BMJ Publishing Group 1994

First published in 1994
by the BMJ Publishing Group, BMA House,
Tavistock Square, London WC1H 9JR

British Library Cataloguing in Publication Data

A catalogue record for this book is available
from the British Library
ISBN-0-7279-0879-0

This work was originally sponsored by the West Midlands Postgraduate Board of Medical and Dental Education and distributed to all house officers free of charge.

Typeset in Great Britain by Apek Typesetters Ltd.,
Avon House, Blackfriars Road, Nailsea

Contents

Acknowledgements

I would like to thank the House Officers at the Queen Elizabeth Medical Centre, who gave up what little free time they had to comment on this book.

Also, *Coping with Stress – a Handbook for Trainees in Clinical Psychology*, which provided the inspiration.

CG

The cartoons are by Malcolm Willett. The author and publishers are grateful to the artist and the Student Edition of the *BMJ*, in which they first appeared, for permission to reproduce them.

About this book

Hello and welcome to the world of medicine. Whether you are a qualified doctor or a medical student, the chances are that you have been taught a large amount about the theory and practice of medicine. Unfortunately, you will probably not have been taught much, if anything, about looking after yourself, and in particular how to cope with some of the stressful (and often distressing) experiences that will come your way. The purpose of this book is simple:

- to let you know that you are not alone in this
- to pass on some ways that others have coped with similar situations.

My overriding memory of 1 August 1988 was of finding out at 9 am that I was on-call that evening (the rota had only been organised the day before). Come 5 o'clock that day, I was wishing that bleeps had never been invented. By 7 o'clock, I was wondering why I had never been taught the nitty gritty of being a house officer. By the following morning, I was ready to leave the profession. It got better...or perhaps I got better at handling things! Certainly, any new situation, be it a new job or a new student attachment is stressful. This is to be expected, but once you have settled in you will find that things become easier to cope with. Things are never as bad as they may first appear.

This book is divided into two sections – a brief background on what stress is, and how it may affect you; and a brief review of some techniques that others have found useful for dealing with stress. At the back is a list of agencies which provide help. I have tried to keep the book as informal and quick to read as possible. As a result, nothing is formally referenced, though there is a bibliography at the back. I have also included a few quizzes to help you assess whether or not you are stressed, and to look at various ways of coping with stress. Boxed practical hints throughout provide summaries of action you can take.

Most people enjoy their first taste of being a "proper doctor", taking responsibility for their patients, and watching people get better. What they do not enjoy are the long hours, the bleep, being rung in the middle of the night to prescribe two paracetamol tablets, and having to eat hospital food. So, when you feel as if everything is getting on top of you, remember, you are not alone, all of us have felt the same way at some stage and there are ways and means round all stumbling blocks. Just read on for a few ideas.

Understanding stress

Doctors and stress - is there a problem?

Do doctors suffer from stress? The answer to this must surely be "Yes." We are human, and if others can suffer from stress then so can we. In fact, up to 50% of house officers are emotionally disturbed at some time, and perhaps as many as 30% are clinically depressed.

In more dramatic terms, doctors have virtually double the risk of developing cirrhosis of the liver, or committing suicide, compared with the general population. Both of these causes of death are generally regarded as indicators of poor mechanisms for coping with long-term stress.

Stress – what is it?

Stress is one of those things that people recognise in others, but often miss in themselves. It arises when **you** feel unable to cope with whatever is demanded of **you.** For example, being on-call proves very stressful if you are not confident of your ability to deal with whatever comes through the door. If, however, you are confident of your ability to deal with most situations, or have the back-up necessary to help you manage, then the degree of stress you feel will be reduced.

One way of looking at stress is illustrated in figure 1. In this model the individual makes a judgement of threat based on two sets of factors: environmental and individual.

The first set of factors relates to the environment in which you find yourself. This consists of demands placed on you at home, at work, and from your personal life. Don't forget that the balance between these areas of your life will affect your ability to cope with stress. We rarely manage to partition off the various areas of our life.

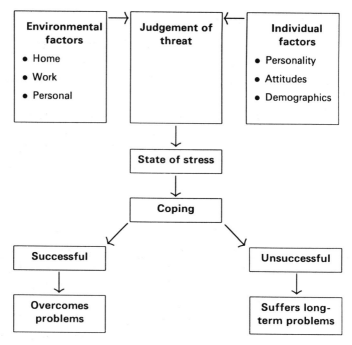

Figure 1 The stress process.

The second set of factors relates to the individual, and includes personality traits (for example, are you an anxious person by nature), and attitudes (for example, believing that to say "I don't know" is a weakness). Other individual factors will include things like age and social class. Generally, the older you get, the more self-confident you become, and the better you perceive your ability to handle situations. This in turn will reduce the amount of stress that you feel.

As I suggested earlier, the judgement of stress is very much an individual process. This explains why one person flourishes under certain circumstances, while another suffers – a case of one man's meat is another man's poison. It is therefore impossible for me, or for that matter anyone else, to tell you when a situation is or is not stressful. Only you can decide whether or not it is.

The outcome of stress

Looking further down the stress model, you can see that there are two outcomes: successful and unsuccessful. The successful ways of coping with stress generally allow you either to put behind you whatever caused the problem, or to know how to deal with it in a more constructive way in the future. The unsuccessful methods of coping with stress result in long-term problems, such as psychological and emotional distress, depression, suicide, and possibly asthma, common colds, and heart disease.

Depression and suicide

One tragic consequence of not managing stress appropriately is suicide. Doctors have a 72% increased risk of killing themselves compared with the general population. In common with other health care professionals, this is often by the use of drugs, and probably reflects the fact that these items are accessible, and that doctors have the expert knowledge to use them effectively.

Depression is related to the issue of suicide. Over the course of a lifetime, a minimum of one in five people will be diagnosed as suffering from a depressive illness. Doctors, being part of the human race, are not exempt from this. Obviously, stress will not necessarily be the cause of

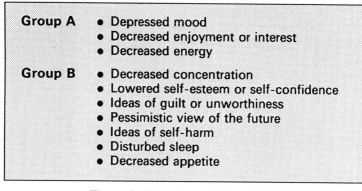

Group A	• Depressed mood
	• Decreased enjoyment or interest
	• Decreased energy
Group B	• Decreased concentration
	• Lowered self-esteem or self-confidence
	• Ideas of guilt or unworthiness
	• Pessimistic view of the future
	• Ideas of self-harm
	• Disturbed sleep
	• Decreased appetite

Figure 2   Symptoms of depression.

depression, although it may exacerbate the illness, and indeed seeking help may be a further source of stress.

Having said that depression is a simple fact of life for many people, how do you recognise it? Figure 2 shows some of the classical symptoms of depression, although not everyone experiencing depression will exhibit them. It is generally considered that if you have suffered from two symptoms in the A group and two or more symptoms in the B group for two weeks or more, then you are likely to be suffering from depression. It is important to remember that many people will occasionally exhibit one of these symptoms, without suffering from depression.

The good news about depression is that people generally recover from it spontaneously, often without requiring drug treatment. Nevertheless, it is by definition a fairly miserable illness and one that is readily amenable to treatment. It is unfortunate, however, that doctors seem to have difficulty in asking for that help before things get out of hand.

Stress – is it always bad?

Having spent so long telling you that stress is bad for you, I think it is only fair to say that stress can, in fact, be good for you. Stress can increase drive and energy. It can be a creative force. If you do not experience some stress, then you are unlikely to achieve much in life.

To illustrate the positive nature of stress, think about taking finals. Three months before them there is very little incentive for you to revise, you are under little stress. This changes dramatically the closer towards the exams you get. Two weeks before finals you will be sufficiently stressed by impending disaster to at least think about doing some work. If you start working at this stage, you will probably be working quite efficiently. However, if you leave doing any work until two days before the exams, then the threat and stress caused by having so little time, and so much to do, means that you are unlikely to do any constructive revision.

Figure 3 illustrates the graphical nature of stress. On the left-hand side of the curve, too little stress results in minimal performance. On the right of the graph, too much stress results in very poor performance. As the middle of the graph shows however, a certain amount of stress results in peak performance. Again, it is up to you to judge how much stress is appropriate for you to work efficiently.

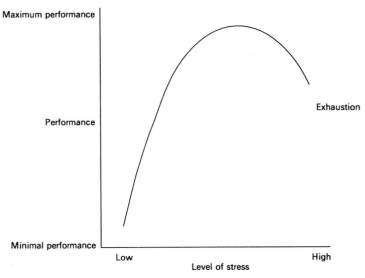

Figure 3   The performance curve.

7

Minor stress *versus* major stress

Virtually everyone can appreciate that major events such as the death of a spouse or moving house can cause stress. However, it is worth remembering that many minor stressors may be more difficult to deal with than one major stressor. Cumulative stress may be less easy to come to terms with as it affects more areas of your life.

How stressed are you?

The following quiz (figure 4) is designed to help you assess your current position in the stress stakes. Put a cross in the "Yes" column for each event which has taken place in the last two years and then rate how upsetting you found it on a scale of 1 to 10 (1 = very little, 10 = a lot). At the end, sum up your score and plot it on the scale. (Source: Cooper CL, Cooper R, Saragher EB. *Psych Med* 1989:**19**:415–22.)

Recognising stress

In order to deal with stress you have to do two things:

● recognise when you are suffering from stress
● know what caused that stress.

In this section I am going to look at some of the symptoms and signs seen when someone is suffering from stress.

Often, one of the first signs that someone is stressed is a change in some aspect of their character. There are four major groups of effects caused by stress. These are physical effects, emotional effects, effects on thinking and effects on behaviour. The types of effects are listed in figure 5, and you may find it useful to note how many of these things you have experienced.

You will probably recognise at least some of the effects of stress in yourself. You will experience different effects at different times depending on the sort of stress that you are under at that particular time. This is entirely normal. For

Event	Yes Score
Bought house	...... 1 2 3 4 5 6 7 8 9 10
Sold house	...... 1 2 3 4 5 6 7 8 9 10
Moved house	...... 1 2 3 4 5 6 7 8 9 10
Major house renovation	...... 1 2 3 4 5 6 7 8 9 10
Separation from loved one	...... 1 2 3 4 5 6 7 8 9 10
End of relationship	...... 1 2 3 4 5 6 7 8 9 10
Got engaged	...... 1 2 3 4 5 6 7 8 9 10
Got married	...... 1 2 3 4 5 6 7 8 9 10
Marital problem	...... 1 2 3 4 5 6 7 8 9 10
Awaiting divorce	...... 1 2 3 4 5 6 7 8 9 10
Divorce	...... 1 2 3 4 5 6 7 8 9 10
Child started school/nursery	...... 1 2 3 4 5 6 7 8 9 10
Problems with relatives	...... 1 2 3 4 5 6 7 8 9 10
Increased nursing responsibilities for elderly or sick person	...... 1 2 3 4 5 6 7 8 9 10
Problems with friends/neighbours	...... 1 2 3 4 5 6 7 8 9 10
Pet related problems	...... 1 2 3 4 5 6 7 8 9 10
Work related problems	...... 1 2 3 4 5 6 7 8 9 10
Change in nature of work	...... 1 2 3 4 5 6 7 8 9 10
Threat of redundancy	...... 1 2 3 4 5 6 7 8 9 10
Changed job	...... 1 2 3 4 5 6 7 8 9 10
Made redundant	...... 1 2 3 4 5 6 7 8 9 10
Retired	...... 1 2 3 4 5 6 7 8 9 10
Increased or new bank loan or mortgage	...... 1 2 3 4 5 6 7 8 9 10
Financial difficulty	...... 1 2 3 4 5 6 7 8 9 10
Insurance problem	...... 1 2 3 4 5 6 7 8 9 10
Legal problem	...... 1 2 3 4 5 6 7 8 9 10
Emotional or physical illness of close family or relative	...... 1 2 3 4 5 6 7 8 9 10
Serious illness of close family or relative requiring hospitalisation	...... 1 2 3 4 5 6 7 8 9 10
Death of spouse or partner	...... 1 2 3 4 5 6 7 8 9 10
Death of family member or relative	...... 1 2 3 4 5 6 7 8 9 10
Death of close friend	...... 1 2 3 4 5 6 7 8 9 10
Serious illness requiring your own hospitalisation	...... 1 2 3 4 5 6 7 8 9 10
Surgical operation on yourself	...... 1 2 3 4 5 6 7 8 9 10
Pregnancy	...... 1 2 3 4 5 6 7 8 9 10

Assessment scale

Low stress   High stress
├──────────┼──────────┤
1   50   100

Figure 4   Stress quiz.

9

Physical effects
- The TATT syndrome (tired all the time)
- Headaches
- Backache
- Constipation or diarrhoea
- Sweating
- Dry mouth
- Palpitations
- Tight chest
- Nausea and vomiting
- Not being able to sleep
- Increased or decreased appetite

Emotional effects
- Feeling high or low
- Getting agitated or feeling fatalistically calm
- Hostility
- Feeling guilty
- Feeling frustrated
- Feeling anxious
- Feeling apathetic
- Feeling useless, or feeling threatened or attacked in some way
- Getting irritable and losing your sense of humour

Effects on thinking
- The little devil on your shoulder shouting "failure"
- Fearfulness
- Becoming obsessive
- Black and white thinking
- Everything is either a total success or a total failure
- Self attribution (i.e. all failure is due to me, all success due to others)
- Lack of concentration
- Thought blocks and loss of short-term memory

Effects on behaviour
- Overeating or not eating
- Drinking to excess
- Smoking
- Becoming argumentative or aggressive
- Driving too fast
- Not bothering
- Loss of interest in sex
- Becoming cold and offhand, particularly with loved ones
- Becoming over-demanding of affection

Figure 5 The effects of stress.

example, before standing up to give a presentation many people will suffer from a dry mouth, butterflies in the stomach, sweaty palms, and perhaps palpitations or a feeling that they are unable to breathe easily. Those same people on walking into a roomful of people they do not know may well become over-loud, laugh a lot, and speak too loudly. Both sets of symptoms are indicative of stress. In a similar way you may cry at one funeral but be withdrawn and apparently unemotional at another. Again, both are symptomatic of stress but result from different ways of coping with stress at different points in life.

Stress – what causes it?

Having recognised that you suffer from stress, we can now begin to look at some of the common causes of stress. These factors are known as stressors. These, as you may have guessed, vary from person to person and from time to time. What stressed you at 21 may not stress you at 42 and *vice versa*.

We have already seen that stress occurs when there is an imbalance between environmental and personal factors, and how these are judged by the individual. It is an unfortunate fact of life that doctors have, and are trained to have, certain characteristics which are known to exacerbate the effects of stress. As Kilburg said, "Professionals can be their own worst enemies. Trained to be independent, creative, assertive, competitive, and hard driving. They do not readily acknowledge that they are in trouble or need assistance" (Kilburg R In: Kilburg R, Nathan PE, Thoreson RW (eds). *Professionals in Distress* American Psychological Association, 1986, 25).

Occupational stressors

There are many types of stressors. They can be general occupational stressors, for example factors intrinsic to the job; or can be related to organisation, career development, and role and relationships within the job. Figure 6 lists some of the stressors generally recognised within the medical profession and those more specific to junior doctors, and to medical students.

You can see that some of these stressors are intrinisc to the job: for example dealing with death and dying, being nice to people you may not like, talking to distressed relatives. Others are very much more related to the organisation or structure within which we work, that is the NHS. Examples of these organisational factors may include spending half your night

11

Job hopping.

finding beds for patients, and moving house in order to pursue the career you wish to. Added to which, changes within the NHS and the uncertainty this brings create pressure. As a house officer you may not be as acutely aware of some of these types of stressors as are more senior doctors who undertake a managerial role. These people will frequently experience a conflict of loyalty towards their employers, particularly their non-medical manager, their colleagues, and their patients.

Personal and academic stressors

There are other forms of stressors outside the work environment. These may be academic stressors, with which you will be very familiar, for example exams, the amount of academic work, and the need to achieve good grades.

Additionally, there are personal factors which will act as stressors. These occur frequently in medicine because of the organisation of the profession. Examples include the need to move house often, the need to move to a new area, the need to find a new social network, separation from spouse or partner, time away from family, not enough time for recreation and so on.

These types of stressor often become more apparent in the middle stages of your career, when the support networks you

Generally recognised
- Face to face contact with people
- Death, dying, distress, and disability
- Long hours of work and shiftwork
- Performing traumatic, invasive, intimate medical procedures
- Increasing moral and ethical dilemmas
- Increasing technology
- Responsibility for people, not objects
- Self doubts about responsibility for medical failure
- Enormous consequences of wrong decisions, in terms of both emotions and litigation
- Risk of occupationally acquired illness
- Risk of physical violence, for example in accident and emergency departments
- Public expectation and demand
- Pay differences between team members leading to dissatisfaction and tension within a team
- Interference by government and management
- Inflexibility, unpredictable career path, inability to change specialty without substantial retraining and uncertainty of obtaining consultant grade posts
- Conflict between professional role and personal values/conscience
- Conflict of loyalty

Specific to junior doctors
- Inadequately defined roles
- Overwork
- Talking to distressed relatives
- Effects on personal life
- Serious treatment failures
- Poor relations with consultants and other senior medical staff
- Having too few skills
- Poor living conditions
- Lack of support and supervision
- Job insecurity
- Conflict between work and family
- Accessibility to further professional education
- Inexperience
- Career progression
- Alienation from family and social life
- Fear of litigation

Specific to medical students
- Constant evaluation of skills by patients, consultants, and other staff
- Long hours
- Many exams
- Financial pressures
- Career worries
- Information overload
- Disillusionment with chosen career path
- Competition between students

Figure 6   Stressors affecting doctors.

formed as a medical student fail and you do not yet have the support of a partner and family. For example, people you know move on, you move to new areas, and work in hospitals where you do not know the system, and are working with new people.

Self-esteem

Another set of stressors is related to self-esteem or self-worth. Medicine by its nature tends to be fairly challenging. You need to have a reasonable amount of self-confidence to be able to stand up and do presentations in front of peers (also known as the ward round), to be able to handle distressed people, to be able to delegate without actually being in a position of authority to delegate (otherwise known as negotiation). You are required to deal with situations that you may never have come across before, or to perform procedures that you have perhaps only seen once before (the see one, do one, teach one mentality is still so widespread in medicine). All of these challenges, with which you will be confronted on a day-to-day basis, require someone with a high level of self-confidence and self-esteem to handle them well. Nearly all doctors are at times uncertain of their own capabilities and pressure from peers and superiors can heighten this level of uncertainty. Add to this the fear of failure, or of being made to feel a fool, and the threat of litigation, and, without perhaps being consciously aware of it, you are already under a fair amount of stress.

Peer pressure

Never underestimate peer pressure. In medical school everyone sits exams at much the same time, and about the only competition between people is whether or not they intercalate degrees, or where they go on their elective. When professional exams start, you will be surprised at the amount of pressure there is to sit them at the earliest time possible, often against a background of working long hours, and a pass rate of perhaps only 30%. This is another form of stress. Other examples of peer pressure include the race to reach the next rung of the career ladder, to complete your MD, or to have papers published.

Women doctors

Women doctors have additional stressors to their male counterparts. These include conflicts between home and work; problems with child care; inflexibility of the career structure to accommodate part-time training and maternity leave; sexual harassment; prejudice from patients (who consider all women to be nurses); and lack of female role models.

Medical students

Someone once said that all medical schools should have a health warning attached to them. Undoubtedly, the medical course is a demanding one, and one that many people feel does not equip you properly to do the job that will be first asked of you – that of pre-registration House Officer.

However, there is more to it than that. Medical students differ from other students in many ways. They have longer terms and a longer course. The hours they work are longer than most other students and they take more exams than most other students. They are required from an early stage to deal with the public, and in particular to deal with distressed people and distressing circumstances, such as death and severe disability. Not only are they required to demonstrate academic competence but also practical competence, learning and practising (again at an early stage in their careers) unpleasant rituals on their fellow students.

Arguably, all this and more, has been asked of medical students for many years. However, even if the closed world of medical school stays still, the outside world moves on. Students now face the prospect of lower grants, with many having to take outside jobs or take on loans in order to finance themselves through university. Medicine continues to advance at an extraordinary rate, and these advances have to be accommodated in an already overstretched curriculum.

As a result many medical students find themselves in stressful situations, particularly relating to money, choice of career path and exams.

Managing stress

Many of the stressors affecting the medical profession are inherent in their work and are therefore unavoidable. Under such circumstances, it is important that you find ways to manage stress rather than allowing it to manage you.

The theory of stress management is simple. First identify priorities, goals, and problems; then learn to come to terms with difficulties and circumstances. You will face stress of one sort or another throughout your career in medicine, therefore it is worth taking a long term view of your situation, and trying to understand your reaction to it.

Identifying the causes of stress

Before you can begin to deal with stress, you first have to recognise that you are suffering from stress, and then work out what has caused it. One way of doing this is through keeping a stress diary. This involves keeping a record of situations which you found stressful, noting who was involved, what you did and what you would have rather done. Try to do this for a period of four weeks. This requires a degree of self-discipline (asking a stressed person to find the time for such a task is akin to offering a drowning man a glass of water) but it will reap benefits in the long term.

At the end of this time, try to identify types of incidents and the type of person involved. Then attempt to think of a plan of action to prevent similar events happening again. An example would be not having results available on a ward round, being shouted at, becoming increasingly nervous of ward rounds, and forgetting results. Ways of dealing with this might include: ensuring all results are filed; having a crib sheet of abnormal results; handing the notes to the consultant to look up the result for himself; and (if you are feeling brave or foolhardy) telling him that he would get a far better service from you if he did not shout. Further details of how to keep a stress diary can be found in *Living with Stress* (see Bibliography).

Stress – how do you cope?

There are different ways of responding to stress. You can adapt to it successfully, adapt temporarily, or not adapt at all. Figure 7 will give you an idea of the different types of adaptation, and which variety you make use of. Simply circle the number which most closely matches how frequently you use that particular coping mechanism, sum the scores and plot them on the scale given.

Temporary adaptation

Temporary adaptation can be a very effective mechanism for dealing with short term stressors. Many of us have bought ourselves a treat after a particularly bad week, or gone out in the evening to enjoy ourselves, and felt very much better for it.

Maladaptation

Maladaptation to stress is, quite simply, bad for you. However, it may be a temporary phase through which you pass on your way to long term adaptation. One example of this is leaving a long term relationship when it is very common not to sleep, not to eat, perhaps to drink heavily, and to fantasise about what might have been. The majority of people will come to terms with what has happened and take up more appropriate and adaptive behaviours in due course. Obviously, those who fail to adapt are storing up problems for themselves.

Stress – keeping it at bay

There are many strategies for coping with stress, and for that matter distress. Those in the caring professions are, as a rule, very poor at looking after themselves, and at looking after one

Temporary adaptation

Get on with work, keep busy	1	2	3	4	5
Throw yourself into work	1	2	3	4	5
Do some housework	1	2	3	4	5
Try to do something where you don't use your mind	1	2	3	4	5
Cry on your own	1	2	3	4	5
Bottle it up, then break down	1	2	3	4	5
Explosive, mostly temper not tears	1	2	3	4	5
Treat yourself to something, for example clothes	1	2	3	4	5

Key: 1 = never, 2 = rarely, 3 = periodically, 4 = regularly, 5 = very often

Adaptive behaviour

Sit and think	1	2	3	4	5
Ability to cry with friends	1	2	3	4	5
Get angry with people or things which cause the problem	1	2	3	4	5
Let feeling out, talk to close friends	1	2	3	4	5
Talk things over with lots of friends	1	2	3	4	5
Go over and over the problem to try to understand it	1	2	3	4	5
Feel that you learn something from every distress	1	2	3	4	5
Talk to someone who may be able to help	1	2	3	4	5
Try to get sympathy and understanding from someone	1	2	3	4	5

Key: 1 = never, 2 = rarely, 3 = periodically, 4 = regularly, 5 = very often

Maladaptive behaviour

Try not to think about it	5	4	3	2	1
Go quiet	5	4	3	2	1
Go on as if nothing had happened	5	4	3	2	1
Keep feelings to yourself	5	4	3	2	1
Avoid being with people	5	4	3	2	1
Show a brave face	5	4	3	2	1
Worry constantly	5	4	3	2	1
Lose sleep	5	4	3	2	1
Don't eat	5	4	3	2	1
Control tears (hide feelings)	5	4	3	2	1
Eat more	5	4	3	2	1
Wish you could change what happened	5	4	3	2	1
Have fantasies about how things could have turned out	5	4	3	2	1

Key: 1 = very often, 2 = regularly, 3 = periodically, 4 = rarely, 5 = never

```
Maladaptive                    Adaptive
|-------------------+-------------------|
29                 87                  145
```

Figure 7 How do you adapt to stress? (Source: Cooper CI, Cooper R, Eaker L. *Living with Stress*. London: Penguin, 1988.)

another. One example of this is the reluctance that doctors feel to take time off work when they are ill because of the effects this will have on their peers, who, as a result may have to reduce their time off, may have to do an on-call at short notice, and will have to add your workload to their own.

Acknowledging stress

Probably the most important thing about managing stress is to recognise that you are suffering from it and to

> **Dealing with stress**
> ● Acknowledge stress
> ● Keep a balance between work and outside life
> ● Find a good confidant
> ● Keep a network of friends and acquaintances
> ● Look after yourself
> ● Ask for help if you need it

acknowledge that it is acceptable to do so. Often acknowledging and talking about things reduces their impact considerably. By talking, you may pick up how other people have handled similar sorts of situations and you may be able to apply this to your own problem.

Below are a few mechanisms which people have found useful in learning to cope with stressful situations. Not all are appropriate in all situations, or for all people. It is a question of choice. The chances are that you are already using some of these techniques in some shape or form. If you are not, then ask yourself how you are managing your stress – or is it managing you?

Need for balance

There is a tendency in medicine to believe that if you are not working 24 hours a day, 365 days a year on medicine, then you are not doing your job properly. I shall remain polite and call it a fallacy.

Everyone has different needs and wants in life. A career, even a vocational one, is usually only part of a person's life. It is important that you recognise that time out from medicine, time for yourself and time for other people outside medicine is important. Those people who find time to do things outside medicine often comment on how useful they find it, saying that it nearly always brings a new perspective to problems which are encountered on a day-to-day basis. Additionally, it creates relationships outside the medical profession or health professions which can be immensely supportive.

Need for a confidant

A close personal relationship, be it with a spouse, partner, or a significant other person, is important. A good confidant is someone with whom you can talk over both professional and personal difficulties. It should be a person to whom you can unload problems, for example to moan about the boss or about other doctors whom you consider are not pulling their weight. You should also be able to talk about your feelings with your confidant. Some things that you see or do or hear about will upset you. One example of this, which is faced by all doctors at some point in their career, is the patient who dies. The doctor may feel considerable sadness at the death, perhaps because it is someone they had been caring for over a long period of time, or someone they consider has faced up bravely to some challenge. Other doctors feel tremendous guilt when a patient dies, perhaps because of something they have (or feel they have) done incorrectly, or omitted to do, or because the patient died in distress and pain.

Having said that a confidant can provide all of this and more, it is important to recognise that a confiding relationship takes a lot of working at. Time must be found. The confidence will often have to be reciprocated. Sometimes you will need to seek permission from your confidant to talk through certain issues. Sometimes your confidant will have to ask you what is troubling you because you will consider it not worth troubling them about your worries. All of these types of issues take time, trust and care to develop.

Need for a network

No man is an island, as the saying goes, and doctors are no different from others. Nearly all of us have many relationships, on many levels, with many different people. There will be close intimate relationships with spouses and partners, intimate friendships, people you go down to the pub with, and people you are on nodding terms with. Additionally there will be a network of people who play different roles in your life – friends, relatives, confidants, lover, boss, manager and so on.

This group of people can provide support, a balanced perspective and accurate feedback, and reduce the vulnerability inherent in a single relationship. It is important to try to include a variety of people in your network. Family members, for instance, are often prepared to give feedback where friends are not. Peers provide a point of view from a perspective similar to your own, something that parents may not be able to do. Colleagues can understand and empathise with professional experiences and are usually prepared to put problems in perspective, for example by telling you to stop persecuting yourself over the fact that it took you three attempts to get blood from a patient yesterday.

You and your consultant

This is, needless to say, an important relationship, but one in which there is often a considerable degree of conflict.

Much of the success of the relationship will depend on the success that you have had with authority figures in the past. It is unfortunate that most medical students are regarded as a life form only slightly higher than the amoeba, and previous encounters with consultants tend to have been somewhat strained. The qualities which the junior doctor will often need in this relationship are those of assertiveness and self-esteem. Assertive people who believe that they are inherently worthwhile will tend to form mutually respectful relationships with their consultants. More about this later.

Just as the characteristics that the junior brings to a relationship influence it, so will the characteristics that the consultant brings. In particular the consultant's attitude to power and authority, and specifically their experience with it; their feelings of self-esteem, notably their own fear of failure or poor performance; and quite possibly the need to make another feel small in order to make themselves feel big. These attitudes and feelings will affect their attitudes towards such

23

things as time off, and cross cover and hence influence how decent the job is.

Another aspect of the relationship between junior doctor and consultant is that your consultant will wear many hats within your relationship. There will be that of tutor, that of mentor, perhaps that of personal tutor, and certainly that of referee. These different roles are sources of potential conflict: do you want to talk to your consultant about feeling upset when, at the end of six months, you have to ask him or her to act as a referee for you? Similarly, time may never be available in which to ask for help or supervision. Additionally, junior posts rarely last for more than six months with any particular consultant and this constrains the degree to which a relationship can and will develop. Many people decide that there is not enough time to invest too much in a relationship with their consultant.

Need for self-care

Many doctors find it difficult to shrug off the role of carer. As a result they find themselves listening to friends, colleagues and acquaintances asking them about their backaches, their knee problems, whether they should have their varicose veins done or not, and so on. This, not surprisingly, becomes very tiring, and leaves many people with a feeling that they are constantly on duty, and unable to take time out to care for themselves. This can be rather harmful.

As you may expect, the recommendations for self-care are a classic example of "do as I say and not as I do" for most doctors. Long hours and hospital canteens make eating a balanced diet fairly difficult. Being on-call involves reduced hours of sleep, and when you do sleep it is often just a doze because you are wondering when the bleep is going to go off again. Traditional teaching about healthy life-styles often appears to take all the fun out of life. However, the following life-style hints could be achieved by even the most fallible of us.

Do not smoke or use drugs. These substances are frequently used as mechanisms to cope with stress. Relief is only temporary and continued use may lead to a reduction in your overall quality of life.

Go easy on the alcohol. Work out how much you drink – the answer may surprise you. The maximum recommended weekly limit is 14 units for women and 21 for men (1 unit is a glass of wine, a half pint of ordinary beer, or a standard measure of spirits).

Eat a balanced diet. Find time to eat regularly, no matter how busy you are. Avoid junk foods and aim for a diet which is low in fat, sugar and salt and high in fibre. Never go without a meal. Food not only provides energy, but eating gives you a breathing space during a busy day.

Take regular exercise. Try not to be a couch potato on your nights off – any exercise is better than none.

Develop outside interests and hobbies. Participating in a favourite activity or hobby (sex?) can be helpful in releasing built-up tension.

Posture. Stress often shows itself in the ways we sit, walk, and move. Take time to notice your posture. Do you tend to hunch your shoulders or to drop your head as you sit or walk? If so, adjust your posture to make yourself more comfortable.

Holidays. Never go without holidays. Plan them, and book time off well in advance so that you do not face battles about getting cover arranged on the day before you leave. Organise things so that only one person is off at a time – that way those who are left are not overworked.

Register with a general practitioner. Even doctors need a doctor.

Doctors as patients – asking for help

Doctors are not good at asking for help for any form of illness, mental or physical. Generally, doctors are firm believers in self-medication and self-diagnosis. This practice is not good management for any illness and particularly not for mental illness. There are many reasons why doctors fail to seek help, for example concerns about confidentiality, being branded a failure or, even worse, a neurotic unemployable wreck. On a practical level, many doctors, particularly junior doctors who are moving from job to job on a six monthly basis, do not bother to register with a general practitioner. Others consider themselves to be so busy that it is not possible (or they do not wish) to take time off in order to look after their own health. These excuses are all fallacies: a sick doctor does no one any good, neither themselves, their patients nor their colleagues.

The reality of seeking treatment, however, is usually very different from the thought of it. Every patient, whether doctor or not, is entitled to the same degree of confidentiality and indeed has grounds for complaint if this is not met. Doctors are rarely objective about their own health. Generally the life threatening condition they fear they have is reduced to more manageable proportions when subjected to another doctor's objectivity. In short, very often the only person stopping a sick doctor seeking help is the sick doctor themself.

Turning to mental illness, in particular depression. As mentioned earlier, it is a common condition and readily treatable. Most minor depressive illness can be, and is, treated by the general practitioner. Most doctors will go to extraordinary lengths to protect another doctor's confidentiality: psychiatrists may see doctors in their homes or in private rooms rather than at NHS clinics, others offer an informal service to their colleagues.

Although your general practitioner should be your first port of call if you think you are suffering from a depressive illness, there are other sources of help if this is not practical. One source

---

Sources of help with depression
- GP
- Occupational Health Service
- National Sick Doctor's Counselling Service
- British Association for Counselling
- Samaritans
- Mind

---

of help is the Occupational Health Service. Another, outside the realms of work entirely, is the National Sick Doctor's Counselling Service, a completely confidential counselling service in which a sick doctor is paired with a colleague in a different geographical location to act as a confidant and adviser. The names and addresses of other organisations that offer help can be found at the back of this book.

Depression is an illness just like any other. Having depression does not mean that you are a failure, worthless or cannot cope with a career in medicine. Seeking treatment may not be easy, but it is important.

Assertiveness techniques

Stress may arise if you feel put upon in some way, or unable to express your point of view. Assertiveness allows you to be more effective in your dealings with others and so helps to reduce stress. It is about being open and honest about your needs, wants, and feelings, while respecting the fact that others also have needs, wants, and feelings. It is not the same as aggressiveness or bossiness! The basic rights of an individual are listed in figure 8.

There is a fundamental difference between non-assertiveness, aggression, and assertiveness. In brief, when you are assertive you acknowledge your rights as well as other people's; when aggressive you deny the rights of others; and when non-assertive you deny your own rights.

```
You have the right
• to make mistakes
• to set your own priorities
• for your feelings and needs to be considered as
  important as the needs of others
• to refuse requests without feeling guilty
But do not forget that others have the same rights too!
```

Figure 8   Your rights.

Take, for example, the situation of having to ask for neuro obs to be carried out half hourly (a task hated by nurses!).

- *Assertive*   "Jane, I'd like you to do half hourly neuro obs on this patient please, and let me know if ..."
- *Non-assertive* "I know you're very busy, um ... but I wonder if you could possibly ... um ... manage neuro obs on this patient ... um ... as often as you've time for really ..."
- *Aggressive*   "You should know that this patient needs neuro obs!"

Becoming assertive requires a change in behaviour, something which a lot of people find difficult. It can be made even more difficult if people start calling you bossy. Assertiveness teachers will tell you that this is the other person's problem, not yours. Sometimes, however, it means that you have replaced non-assertiveness with aggression, so be warned!

Relaxation techniques

Most doctors face stressful situations which cannot be easily solved: you have to manage the stress. One way of doing this is to learn how to relax physically. Relaxation alone will not cure stress, but learning to relax will make you better prepared for dealing with the practical problems that are often associated with stress.

Relaxation techniques have to be learnt and practised. Relaxation does not mean flopping in front of the television.

Breathing techniques
- Lie down on the floor with the knees bent and spine straight.
- Scan body for tension
- Inhale slowly and deeply, feeling your abdomen slightly rise with each inhalation
- Inhale through your nose and exhale gently through your mouth making a relaxing whooshing sound
- Focus on the sound of your breathing, then on the rise and fall of your abdomen and the deepening sense of relaxation
- Let other thoughts and distractions pass in and out of your mind
- Practise daily and use whenever you feel tension.

Relaxation script
- Lie on the floor, flat on your back or sit in a comfortable chair.
- Take one or two deep breaths, breathing in through the nose and out through the mouth.
- Then focus your attention on different parts of your body, in turn.
- As your attention moves to each part, allow it to relax.
- Then say to yourself... "head...shoulders...right arm...left arm...stomach and abdomen...right leg...left leg...right foot...left foot...whole body".
- As your attention shifts to each part of the body allow that part to relax completely.

Figure 9 Relaxation techniques.

There are a number of relaxation techniques including simple breathing exercises, relaxation through scripts, exercises in imagery, meditation and yoga. There are many books on the subject. Examples of simple, quick techniques are given in figure 9.

Meditation techniques

Meditation is about developing a peaceful view of life. There are many meditation techniques available with the best known probably being transcendental meditation. Having

Noticing the breaths
- Sit motionless, comfortably and with your eyes closed.
- Breath quietly and gently. Breath in through your nostrils and out through your mouth.
- Let your attention focus on your breathing.
- Begin to count your breaths, from one to ten. Each number is the whole cycle of an inhalation and an exhalation.
- When the breaths have been counted from one to ten, begin to count the next step from one to ten and so on.
- If you are distracted or lose count, simply go back to the beginning and start again.

Figure 10   Meditation technique.

said that, there is no need to practise a particular type of meditation – there are very simple exercises, such as those in figure 10, that work very well.

Meditation has been shown to reduce tension and help relieve stress. However, in order to be effective, it needs to be practised regularly (preferably daily), as should all types of relaxation exercises.

Time management

Time is finite – it cannot be bought, stored or saved.

It has been estimated that it is possible to save between 10 and 20% of our time every day through effective time management. Having said that, I have my doubts about the relevance of time management to doctors, which is unfortunate since lack of time can be a source of stress to many of us. The theory is very sensible but depends to a large part on being able to predict your day, and take time out from being disturbed. Despite these reservations it is possible to manage your time to a certain extent. The most useful ways of managing time that I have discovered are given below.

Lists, lists and more lists. If it is on paper, it is not cluttering up your brain causing worry.

Delegation. Upwards, downwards, and sideways. If someone else can do it, ask them to. See below.

Negotiation. This is necessary when delegating from a position of weakness, for example to nurses and technicians who tell you they are too busy.

Have a schedule. Write up request forms for elective admissions the night before admission. Carry forms on ward rounds and complete them as you go round (ask someone else to write in the notes). Arrive on wards at certain times of the day (particularly over the weekend), and ask that all non-urgent things are left until then. Always do a pre-bed round. Keep on top of the paperwork by doing it little and often. You may hate it, but it pays dividends when the boss wants a result on a ward round.

Prioritise. Must it be done now, is it a life or death situation (the patient's or yours), or can it wait until your next trip to the X-Ray department for example?

Have quiet times. Ask someone else to carry your bleep while you are doing your discharge letters. The letters will be done more quickly if you are not interrupted. Tell wards when you are going for lunch or dinner, and ask them to hold anything non-urgent until later.

Smile sweetly at all old dragons and give them as much advance notice as possible. That way, when you have something to be done urgently, they are more likely to help out.

Ask the advice of others. If you do not know what a serum rhubarb of 104 means, ring up the lab – they are usually very helpful (and it saves you looking a fool). Referrals to physios are always better received when phrased as "please see and assess" rather than "manipulation of left big toe".

Say "No". If you do not have to do it and you do not want to do it, then you have the right to say "No". Just remember to do so pleasantly.

Treat yourself. Busy periods are often also stressful periods, so allow yourself time out. Use that time to do something quite different. Indulge yourself. Do something new. Sometimes we need to do something that suits us and does not involve doing things for others.

Delegation techniques

Delegation is not passing the buck. It means giving others authority and responsibility while retaining accountability – if something goes wrong it will be your neck on the block. In order to delegate, you must consider carefully which tasks you may legitimately hand over to someone else. You must know about your colleagues and staff, their skills and abilities, and their workload. You must be able to explain what is required of them so that they may successfully complete the task. You must be approachable enough for them to say "I can't do that" or "I think I've done it wrong". You must also know how to bail them out if something goes wrong.

Delegating
- Know your staff/colleagues, their skills and limits
- Explain clearly what is required
- Be approachable
- Remember that you are accountable if things go wrong

Examples of tasks which could be delegated include: taking blood, filing, form filling, message running, telephone requests, ECGs, portering, i.v. drug administration, rewriting (but not signing) drug charts, clerking work, and making telephone calls.

Ways of thinking

A gift of time. You will almost certainly find that you spend large amounts of time waiting for things, such as an admission, results from the lab, or late ward rounds. Next time it happens and there is nothing you can do about it, allow yourself the quaintly named "gift of time". Instead of getting bad tempered, and irritable, do something constructive. Use it to plan ahead, to consider your own wishes and plans or even to day dream.

Stop. Stress sometimes leads to circular thinking. Thoughts go round and round (usually about an unpleasant topic) without resolving anything in the process. One way of dealing with this is consciously to choose to think of other things. Some people achieve this by taking a deep breath and saying "Stop". This becomes the necessary injunction to move on mentally to another topic.

Be more open. Remember that you are never alone, no matter what it feels like. If something is bothering you, then it is important to try to sort it out. If you are upset, let it out. Most people find that "a problem shared is a problem halved".

Flexibility and problem solving

The two major stumbling blocks that doctors frequently encounter are: having to solve problems and weigh probabilities; and having to accept that change happens. There are two approaches to these types of problem.

Develop flexibility

There is only one thing certain in life and that is that it will change. The only thing that may surprise you is the speed at which that change happens. Unfortunately, stress tends to make us inflexible and resistant to change, resulting in us having a hard time when the inevitable happens. To develop flexibility you must:

- Enjoy challenge.
- Not long for the "good old days". Hindsight is a peculiar beast – it tends to be rose tinted. Get a better perspective on the past; learn to think of the bad times as well as the good.
- Let go of the past. Past mistakes are just that – past, dead and buried. No amount of wishing can undo what has happened, so learn to let go instead.
- Accurately assess situations. What is required of me? Do I

have the necessary skills? Is there a safe environment where I can try it out? Do I need training or support?

- Know yourself. What are my limits? Do I want to be involved in this? What support will I need?
- Ask for help. What help do I need? Who should I ask?
- Listen to others.
- Learn from the past: how can I do this better? What can I learn from that mistake? How did I tackle it before?
- Look for alternatives. They always exist – it is merely a matter of finding them.
- Set goals. What are your goals? Do not forget personal as well as work ones. Break all change down into manageable chunks, and plan how you can tackle one bit at a time. Prioritise and delegate where you can.
- Look for the positive things you have achieved. Have you learnt something? Have you learnt something about yourself? What new opportunities have arisen?
- Be kind to yourself. Give yourself a pat on the back. Enjoy praise. Look after yourself. Take time out.

Problem solving

Along with change and the need to be flexible comes problem solving. A structured approach to dealing with problems can often help to reduce stress. Develop a structure for problem solving which works for you. The one in the box may help.

- Identify the problem.
- Gather relevant information.
- Analyse the information you collect.
- Think up as many solutions to the problem as possible.
- Consider the alternatives – weigh up the pros and cons.
- Decide on a solution for the problem.
- Develop an action plan.
- Take the first step... and continue.
- Review the outcome.
- Give praise where praise is due – and that includes to yourself.

Some stressful situations

Doctors regularly come across situations which are generally regarded as stressful, for example dealing with dying patients and their relatives. Telling you how to handle those situations is extremely difficult, simply because they affect each of us in different ways. The most important things to remember are that feelings are normal, there is no point in burying them (though there may be an appropriate time and place to deal with them), and that talking to people helps.

Besides these types of stressful situations, there are a few others, that virtually all medical students and doctors will experience, and which are often overlooked as a source of stress: exams, career worries, and finances.

Exams

I once calculated that including all vivas and end of terms tests (performed under exam conditions of course), I had sat about 150 exams in five years at medical school. Exams are something that you get quite good at as a medical student and they do not stop on graduation. Needless to say, when your future career depends on passing exams, they become remarkably stressful events.

Revision techniques

The standard rules when revising for exams are (my apologies for teaching my grandmother to suck eggs):

- Don't cram
- Set a revision timetable
- Keep to it
- Have time off
- Eat and sleep well.

Revision technique
- Keep revision sessions short
- Work at the best time of day for you
- Make notes
- Make your environment comfortable
- Practise exam technique

If you are a typical medical student you are unlikely to obey any of these rules, but instead sit up until 4 am the night before the exam, having started your revision at 10 pm after a trip to the pub. Similarly, graduates will be snatching half an hour at 2 am while waiting for an admission to arrive. Do not worry. The trick to passing exams is finding a method of revision and work that suits you and then sticking to it. A few methods other people have found useful are given below.

- Keep revision sessions short. Most people concentrate adequately for between 20 and 40 minutes at a time. Follow a revision session with a short break before starting again.
- Work at the best time of day for you. If you are a morning person, get up early and work then. If you are a night owl, work later in the evening.
- Use highlighter pens on books and notes. Make notes on things you have read as this helps to consolidate information.
- Reward yourself, be it with a cup of tea, a biscuit or a soak in the bath.
- Make your environment as comfortable as possible. If you work best at a desk then work at a desk, if you work best lying on the bed then do so.
- Make sure your surroundings are warm and quiet. This usually means shutting the door and making sure you are not disturbed.
- Try working with someone for parts of revision, perhaps taking it in turns to "viva" one another.
- Practise exam techniques by writing essays or examining patients.

The exam itself

As far as the exam goes, remember the simple things, like what is expected of you. What does the syllabus cover? What is the structure of the exam? How long will you have per question and so on?

It is particularly important to know the style of the paper: is it in multiple choice, short note, or essay form. Many exams are based on the multiple choice style and a surprising number of people still fail to recognise that these are usually negatively marked, so a wrong answer counts against you. My own preferred style of working through multiple choice questions was to run through the questions quickly, answering those I could straight off (usually about 10 of them), then move on to those that I had to think about or work out, then to those I was not sure about and finally on to those I did not have a clue about. I always worked on the basis that my first answer was usually the correct one, and I always left the examination room the moment I had finished answering the questions, in order to avoid the temptation of going back and changing everything. This system worked for me but will not suit everyone.

If your exams papers require short notes or essays make sure you have allocated the correct amount of time per question. When answering questions most marks are obtained in the first few minutes of writing and certainly in

---

Taking exams
- Know what the syllabus covers
- Know the style of questions (multiple choice, essay)
- Work out the time allowed for each question
- Make your answers easy to read and mark

---

the first page of the answer. It is therefore better to have started every question even if you do not finish them all, as this will lose you marks for style only.

Other simple things to watch for include writing legibly (try using a fountain pen to aid this) and mastering at least some basic grammar. Some examiners comment that blue pen is easier to read than black though you may not have a choice depending on exam regulations. Others suggest writing on alternate lines particularly if you have large writing and on one side of the paper if you tend to press heavily. I find lots of titles and subtitles are useful. I try to keep sentences and paragraphs short. Many people recommend writing essay plans before you start the question but this is a matter of personal preference.

Postgraduate exams

Being a house officer might not be much fun, but at least you do not have to take any exams, and after five years of taking exams, that can be quite a relief. However, become a senior house officer and postgraduate exams rear their ugly heads. If you wish to pursue a medical career you are almost certainly going to have to take further exams and probably undertake some form of research too. The exception to the rule, at present, is for those wishing to become general practitioners. It is still not compulsory to gain membership of the Royal College of General Practitioners before applying for a general practice principal post. However, moves are afoot to change this, bringing general practice in line with all other specialties.

Postgraduate exams are somewhat different from undergraduate exams. While most undergraduate exams are multiple choice style, many postgraduate exams are of the short note or essay type. It is important, therefore, that you practise exam technique and allocate time correctly for short notes and essays so you do not find yourself without the half hour required to write the final answer. The Royal Colleges, or at least those that produce them, will provide syllabuses and details of their postgraduate exams. The techniques of revision outlined above apply to postgraduate exams as well as undergraduate exams, but there are two extra things to watch for:

- You will be revising while trying to work as well. Take extra care to eat properly, sleep, and have time out.
- You are unlikely to be part of a large group of people taking the exam. The support of friends is therefore nowhere near as forthcoming as it was when you were an undergraduate. In fact, not only is there a lack of peer support, but there may well be peer competition, with people seeking to be the first to get their Part I, membership, or fellowship.

Career worries

A major source of stress to many medical students and newly qualified doctors is what to specialise in. Fortunately, by the end of the pre-registration year, many people have decided, but for the remainder it is often a question of trying out different specialties. The good news is that there are many and varied jobs in medicine, and most people find a niche which suits them.

After choice of career path, perhaps the most common difficulty faced, particularly by female doctors, is how to combine family life and a career. Career breaks and part-time work still appear to be looked down on, and a woman combining family life and career may be regarded with suspicion ("She won't pull her weight"). It is unlikely that this attitude will alter radically until there are considerably more women in positions of power and influence. None the less, it is possible to combine family and career, and indeed those people who spend time away from medicine often state that they are able to bring much more back into the job as a result.

Deciding on a career

At the end of the day only you can decide this. However, there are plenty of people around to help.

Postgraduate deans are based in each university and have a specific remit for careers advice. If you want general advice, particularly about part-time work, and training rotations, this may well be the place to start. Similarly clinical tutors, based in almost all hospitals with training posts, will provide advice. Again, advice from this source tends to be general, rather than specific to specialties.

Sources of written information include a booklet produced by the British Medical Association (general advice about all specialties); and leaflets from the Royal Colleges about careers in their specialty.

At the end of the day, the best advice is to talk to people working in the field, preferably at junior and senior levels, preferably including a consultant whom you have worked for and who knows your abilities (will you clip an aneurysm in the Circle of Willis or poke a hole in the brain?). Once you begin to get a feel for which general area you would like to specialise in, get advice about training rotations, syllabuses, and postgraduate exams, and opportunities for part-time training. Then try it out for six months. Whatever happens, do not be afraid to try something different if you think you

---

Sources of career advice
- Postgraduate dean
- Clinical tutors
- Written information (e.g. BMA, Royal Colleges)
- People working in the chosen specialty
- Medical Forum

> **Finding out about your chosen specialty**
> - Training
> - Rotations
> - Syllabus
> - Postgraduate exams
> - Part-time training
> - Job prospects

have made a mistake. It does not reflect badly on you, and far better you get out now than be miserable for the rest of your working life, or have to retrain.

Leaving medicine?

Some people decide that medicine is not for them. This can occur at any stage in a career, and can be extremely stressful. If you feel that this is your situation, take your time making a decision and seek plenty of advice. Try Medical Forum for advice (more general careers advice is also given), or the careers service.

Financial stress

Nearly all students and doctors know what it is like not to have enough money. This problem becomes particularly bad during the undergraduate clinical years, when travelling over long distances, working in peripheral hospitals, having long terms and short holidays with no opportunity to earn extra money makes being short of cash even more of a problem. There is also the problem of having to buy three times as many textbooks as any other student, and having to wear decent clothes. All contribute to a shortage of cash resources. Things ease considerably on graduation, though the problem then becomes how to pay off the debts!

The most sensible way of managing your finances is to stay out of debt if possible. This is easier said than done. It involves looking at your income and your expenditure and

> **Sources of advice for financial worries**
> - Bank manager
> - Citizens Advice Bureau
> - Students' union

working out precisely where the money goes. It also involves checking bank and credit card statements, something many of us fail to do.

If finances are causing you major headaches then you need to talk to someone. Start with the bank manager, who is often remarkably forthcoming in the case of medical students because they have a virtually guaranteed job to go to. Justtrf remember that you will have to pay back loans one day. Most doctors are considered a reasonably good risk for loans and overdrafts.

In the case of students, find out what benefits you are entitled to. Try the Citizens Advice Bureau (look in the yellow pages for the telephone number) or the Students' Union, which usually has a financial counsellor. Parents and elder siblings may be prepared to help you out. Whatever you do, do not let finances get out of hand. Everyone knows that living on a student grant in this day and age is virtually impossible and most people are quite sympathetic. What they are not sympathetic to is the attitude that if you ignore problems they will go away. They will not and in fact will generally get worse, so the earlier you seek help, the easier it is to sort finances out.

A final word

You may have found that reading this book has made you more aware of your own stress, or perhaps you feel that you need help in tackling some aspect of your life. To have acknowledged this is a big step forward in learning how to cope better with stress.

For some people, the most appropriate way forward will be looking at books – the bibliography at the back may prove a useful starting point. For others, the next step will be to seek some form of structured help, such as counselling. Being counselled should not be seen as a sign of failure, but as a sign of being prepared to take the first step on the road to sorting out whatever is troubling you. Again the list of services at the back of the book may point you in the right direction.

Finally, I would like to leave you with two messages.

Asking for help.

- *It happens to us all.*

- *You're not alone – help is available.*

It is unfortunate that the medical profession tends not to look after its members. However, the only way that this will change is by admitting that we are human, that we experience problems, that it is okay to admit to them, and that we have to take care of ourselves if we are to provide a good service to our patients. The more people who are willing to be open about their experiences, then the faster that change will come about.

Sources of help

The following are all sources of help in times of trouble and stress. Besides the formal organisations, there are a number of informal networks, however, these tend to be of variable quality.

Careers advice

Each university has a postgraduate dean whose specific remit is to provide careers advice and guidance. Your local university will be able to give you further details.

Additionally, most hospitals have clinical tutors who are part of the postgraduate system. These senior doctors are also a useful source of help and advice.

Medical Forum

This is an independent careers advisory service. It was set up and is run by and for doctors.

Greyhound House
23–24 George Street
Richmond
Surrey TW9 1HY
Tel. 0181 332 1234

British Medical Association

The BMA provides a very useful booklet about careers in medicine *(Medical Careers: A General Guide)*. It also provides personal advice and assistance to members, and where appropriate representation to and on behalf of members on most matters related to medical practice, particularly on employment, management training, ethics, locums, legal advice, and information on appropriate courses available throughout Europe.

BMA House
Tavistock Square
London WC1H 9JP
Tel. 0171 387 4499

Legal advice

All medico-legal problems should be discussed with the consultant concerned, and your defence body.

Medical Defence Union
3 Devonshire Place
London W1N 2EA
Tel. 0171 486 6181

Medical Protection Society
50 Hallam Street
London W1N 6DE
Tel. 0171 637 0541

General legal advice can be obtained through the Citizens Advice Bureau, or from solicitors. See the local yellow pages for details.

Counselling services

National Counselling Services for Sick Doctors

This is a confidential, independent counselling service for sick doctors, which is supported by the Royal Colleges, the Joint Consultants Committee, the BMA, and other professional bodies. If a doctor is concerned about his/her health, or that of a colleague, confidential advice is obtainable from senior doctors in all branches of the profession.

The advisor will normally be from the same branch of medicine as the doctor-patient but be from a different geographical area. No permanent records are kept and a sick doctor referred by a colleague is entitled to refuse the offer of help.

1 Park Square West
London NW1 4LJ
Tel. 0171 935 5982

British Association for Counselling

This society does not provide individual counselling but gives information on counselling services run by individual counsellors in different areas.

1 Regent Place
Rugby
Warwickshire CV21 2PJ
Tel. 01788 578328

Samaritans

The Samaritans provides a trained counselling service 24 hours a day. It is entirely confidential. The central office is in London (Tel. 0171 734 2800). Telephone numbers of local services can be found in telephone directories.

Alcoholics Anonymous

See the telephone directory or dial directory enquiries for local groups.

Standing Conference on Drug Abuse (SCODA)

This offers a 24 hour Freephone drug problem service giving recorded contact numbers. Tel. 0171 928 9500.

Mind

Mind promotes the interests of people with mental health problems. It provides legal aid, and information and advice services and has over 200 local associations in England and Wales.

15–19 Broadway
Stratford
London E15 4BX
Tel. 0181 519 2122

Relate

Relate provides advice and counselling on personal and marital relationships. Local services can be found in the telephone directory or through directory enquiries. The central office is in London (tel. 0171 580 1087).

Bereavement counselling

CRUSE Bereavement Care
Cruse House
126 Sheen Road
Richmond TW9 1UR
Tel. 0181 940 4818

Statutory bodies

General Medical Council

Colleagues or patients can refer doctors to the Council when it is considered that the doctor's practice is seriously impaired due to health problems. The GMC consider it in the best interest of all parties that the doctors receive expert medical supervision, and if necessary, accept limitations on practice until they return to good health. The procedures which doctors take part in voluntarily are separate from those of the Health Committee. Most doctors referred to the Council have their cases managed under the direction of the screener for health (a medical member of the Council), and never need to appear before the Health Committee. The

Health Committee becomes involved when a doctor fails to co-operate, or when patient safety is involved.

44 Hallam Street
London W1N 6AE
Tel. 0171 580 7642

Other sources of help

Support from senior hospital medical staff to juniors is available, though there is no formal structure and juniors are often reluctant to use this source of advice for fear of damaging future references. The quality of support varies and is largely dependent on individual characters and personalities. Similarly, clinical tutors are another source of support and advice. No formal structure exists, and support is variable.

Occupational Health Service

All health authorities have an occupational health service to which employees have access. Counselling services are sometimes provided.

General practitioners

Many doctors, particularly in their early clinical years, are not registered with a GP. Surgeries may provide in-house counselling services.

Chaplaincy

All hospitals have chaplains who are often experienced in seeing people through difficult times (usually without too much religious overlay).

Bibliography

Back K, Back K. *Assertiveness at work* 2nd ed. London:McGraw Hill, 1991.

BMA. *Stress and the medical profession* London: BMA Scientific Division, 1992.

Burnard P. *Coping with stress in the health professions – a practical guide*. London: Chapman & Hall, 1991.

Cooper CL, Cooper RD, Eaker LH. *Living with stress*. London: Penguin, 1988.

Cushway D, Dodd B, Merian S. *Coping with stress – a handbook for trainees in clinical psychology*. Birmingham: School of Psychology, The University of Birmingham, 1989.

Dowling S, Barrett S. *Doctors in the making: the experience of the pre-registration year*. Bristol: University of Bristol, School for Advanced Urban Studies, 1991.

Firth-Cozens J. Emotional distress in junior house officers. *BMJ* 1987;**295**:533–6.

Firth-Cozens J. Stress in medical undergraduates and house officers. *Br J Hosp Med* 1989;**41**:161–4.

Firth-Cozens J. Sources of stress in women house officers. *BMJ* 1990;**301**:89–91

Garrett S. *Manage your time* London: Fontana, 1985.

Holden R. *Stress busters*. London: Thorsons, 1992.

Jee M, Reason L. *Action on stress at work*. London: Health Education Authority, 1988.

Siewert LJ. *Managing your time*. London: Kogan Page, 1989.

Index